Mr. Mystery

Written by Mairi Mackinnon

Illustrated by Fred Blunt

How this book works

The story of **Mr. Mystery** has been written for your child to read with your help. Encourage your child to read as much as they can, helping to sound out the words and explaining any meanings if they get stuck.

Mr. Mystery came from a faraway land.

There are puzzles after the story, and for these you may need to read the instructions to your child.

You can find out more about helping your child with this book, and with reading in general, on pages 30-31.

Mr. Mystery

Turn the page to start the story.

Mr. Mystery came from a faraway land.

He could juggle with fire,

and walk on his hands.

He could conjure a flock
of doves out of thin air.

For a special occasion,
he had to be there.

We met him one morning – we thought he looked glum.

14

He said, "Children, I'm sorry, the moment has come."

"I've made my decision –
it's time to retire."

"You may laugh, but I've had enough playing with fire."

His final performance
was something to see.

It ended with fireworks
at a quarter to three.

His little blue boat sailed
out on the ocean...

Though nobody saw it
in all the commotion.

A letter arrives from
a faraway land.

"Hope to visit you some day. My new life is grand!"

Mr. Mystery

Puzzle 1

Are these sentences true? Look at the
pictures and say what really happened.
(Look back at the story if you need help.)

1.

Mr. Mystery came from our home town.

2.

He used to scare the birds away at weddings.

3.

He wanted to keep on working forever.

4.

His final performance wasn't very good.

5.

We never heard from him again.

Puzzle 2

Choose from the four words at the bottom of these pages to fill the gaps in the sentences.

1.

We .... he looked glum.

2.

"You may.........."

laugh

Though

3.

"I've had ....
playing with fire."

4.

..........nobody saw it
in all the commotion.

| enough | thought |

Puzzle 3

For each word on the left, there is a shorter word on the right that means the same, or almost the same. Can you find it? The first pair has been linked as an example.

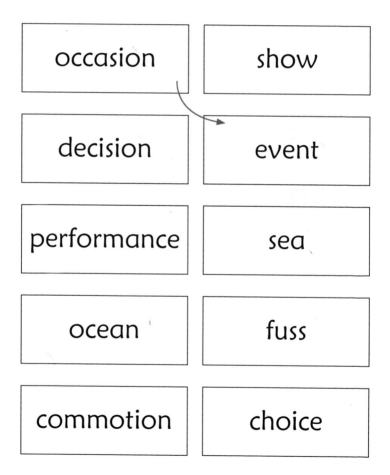

occasion	show
decision	event
performance	sea
ocean	fuss
commotion	choice

Answers to puzzles

Puzzle 1

(Your child doesn't have to use these exact words.)

1. No, he came from a faraway land.

2. No, he could conjure them out of thin air.

3. No, he made his decision to retire.

4. No, his final performance was something to see.

5. No, a letter arrived from a faraway land.

Puzzle 2

1. We <u>thought</u> he looked glum.

2. You may <u>laugh</u>.

3. I've had <u>enough</u> playing with fire.

4. <u>Though</u> nobody saw it in all the commotion.

Puzzle 3

occasion ⟶ event

decision ⟶ choice

performance ⟶ show

ocean ⟶ sea

commotion ⟶ fuss

Guidance notes

Usborne Very First Reading is a series of books, specially developed for children who are learning to read. **Mr. Mystery** is the fifteenth book in the series, and by this stage your child should be able to read the story alone, with occasional help from you.

The story of **Mr. Mystery** introduces the following spelling and pronunciation patterns:

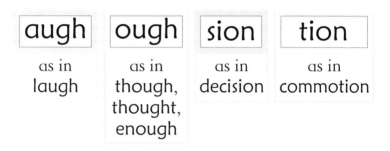

augh	ough	sion	tion
as in laugh	as in though, thought, enough	as in decision	as in commotion

It also gives your child practice in reading longer words (three or four syllables). If your child can read the story comfortably, they are well on the way to independent reading.

You'll find lots more information about the structure of the series, advice on helping your child with reading, extra practice activities and games on the Very First Reading website,* **www.usborne.com/veryfirstreading**

*US readers go to **www.veryfirstreading.com**

Some questions and answers

- **Why do I need to read with my child?**
  Sharing stories makes reading an enjoyable and fun activity for children. It also helps them to develop confidence and stamina. Even if you are not taking an active part in reading, your listening and support are very important.

- **When is a good time to read?**
  Choose a time when you are both relaxed, but not too tired, and there are no distractions. Only read for as long as your child wants to – you can always try again another day.

- **What if my child gets stuck?**
  Don't simply read the problem word yourself, but prompt your child and try to find the right answer together. Similarly, if your child makes a mistake, go back and look at the word together. Don't forget to give plenty of praise and encouragement.

- **We've finished, now what do we do?**
  It's a good idea to read the story several times to give your child more practice and more confidence. Once you are ready to move on, your child might enjoy choosing from the many titles in the **Usborne First Reading** series.

Edited by Jenny Tyler and Lesley Sims
Designed by Caroline Spatz

First published in 2010 by Usborne Publishing Ltd., Usborne House,
83-85 Saffron Hill, London EC1N 8RT, England. www.usborne.com
Copyright © 2010 Usborne Publishing Ltd.

USBORNE VERY FIRST READING

There are over thirty titles in the **Usborne Very First Reading** series, which has been specially developed to help children learn to read. Here are some of them.

To find out more about the structure of the series, go to
www.usborne.com/veryfirstreading